MW00635469

-2019/11/15-

MORE THAN

120

Questions

PART

1

2019

CAT I PREP I SERIES PRACTICE TESTS

Exam Preparation Package

for ISO 18436-2 Certified Vibration Analyst Category I

PRINCIPLES OF VIBRATION

Ali M. Al-Shurafa

Exam Preparation Package for ISO 18436-2 Certified Vibration Analyst (CVA) Category I
Principles of Vibration CAT I PREP I SERIES PRACTICE TESTS (PART 1)
ISBN: 978-1-64415-006-1

Copyright © 2019

All rights reserved. This intellectual asset is legally available only on a hard copy format. No part of this publication may be reproduced, translated, distributed or transmitted in any form or by any means, including photocopying, scanning, or other electronic or mechanical methods, without the prior written permission from the author except as provided by United States of America copyright laws.

Disclaimers

Although every precaution has been taken to verify the accuracy of the information contained herein, the author and publisher assume no responsibility for any errors. No liability is assumed for damages that may result from the use of this package. The question banks in this booklet are related to the standard Body of Knowledge according to ISO Standard 18436-2 Second Edition 2014.

Comments can be sent to info@prepcertify.com

Title	Exam Preparation Package for ISO 18436-2 Certified Vibration Analyst Category I: Principles of Vibration	**Author**	Ali M. Al-Shurafa
Subtitle	Cat I Prep I Part 1	**Series**	CAT I PREP I SERIES PRACTICE TESTS FOR CVA
ISBN-10	1-64415-006-9	**ISBN-13**	978-1-64415-006-1
Publisher	Prep Certify	**Ordering**	www.prepcertify.com

Notes

TABLE OF CONTENTS

Notes

CAT I PREP I PACKAGE AND YOUR CERTIFICATION

This book is Part 1 of 8 parts in Cat I Prep I Package which is designed to help you prepare for and pass the certification exam Vibration Analyst Category I. The internationally recognized standard for this certification is ISO 18436-2 in which the topics of the exam are specified in the Body of Knowledge (BoK) for each category. The majority of certified vibration analysts work in industrial facilities operating rotating equipment. Cat I Prep I Package addresses all topics for Category I in a form of question banks.

This package is unique in several aspects. It is the first package of its kind in this field. It is not biased towards a specific certifying body so all exam candidates can rely on it as a great resource of practice. The question banks of the entire package (Cat I Prep I) include more than 1000 questions which are more than 15 times the questions in a real exam. English Engineering units are used in this package except in a few questions. If SI units are used in this book, they are written after the English units and between brackets e.g. lb (N).

To get the most of Part 1, it is strongly recommended to use it along with the other parts. Each part covers certain topics of the Body of Knowledge according to the ISO standard. Part 1 contains 124 questions, which cover: "Principles of Vibration". Part 8 contains additional information to help you understand the overall certification process and two (2) complete practice exams based on the standard distribution of the questions for each topic.

Cat I Prep I meets and exceeds the standard requirements. For some certifying bodies, some questions in this package are considered suitable for higher levels. Some questions in Cat I Prep I (and in the real exam) may cover more than one topic of the ISO BoK. The overall difficulty of Cat I Prep I is a bit higher than Cat I real exam in order to strengthen the readiness of the candidate before taking the actual exam.

Trainers and certification providers have their preferences for the details of the topics in the BoK. The limited details provided in the Standard give an ample amount of flexibility or gray areas for having questions at different levels. Furthermore, examining the understanding of the same topic can be done in different ways. For these reasons, the difficulty level can vary among the certification exam takers.

The questions are arranged in the

Package to provide the best learning experience. Below are some suggestions and useful tips to follow before you go through the question bank.

1. Study your materials. The best materials could be those provided by your certification body but this is not necessarily true all the times. The optimum study materials should help you answer most of exam questions.

2. Set an environment for a test. This is important to gauge your true readiness for the real exam. Make sure you have the following:

    a. Stopwatch or a timer: On average, each question is expected to take 2 minutes to put your answer on the answer sheet. If you answer the questions in 1 minute/ question, you are fast.

    b. Ruler: You may need a scaled ruler for plots in order to estimate some values like the position of a point with respect to the x axis or y axis.

    c. Simple calculator: No need for a scientific calculator for Cat I certification.

    d. Empty answer sheet: This is provided at the end of the book. A second empty answer sheet is provided if you like to answer the questions for a second time.

e. Dictionary: If you need to translate words to your language, check with your certification body if you can bring a dictionary. Keep in mind that using a dictionary in the exam may delay your progress. So, avoid translation during the exam as much as possible.

f. Formula sheet: For the best preparation, use the approved sheet from your certification body, as it is the one you will use in the real exam. A suggested formula sheet is provided in page 16 if you do not have one. The sheet provided here is good only for Part1.

g. Supporting aids: Use only the approved aids (e.g. tables, charts, sample plots etc.) from your certification body, if this is applicable to your certification.

3. Mark your answers in question page and the answer sheet provided at the end of this book. Follow these tips:

a. Do not keep any question unanswered. There is no penalty for incorrect answers. If you do not answer a question, your score will be zero for that question.

b. Give it a guess, if you cannot answer a difficult question. Put a note next to this question to return to it later. If you have no answer, give it your best guess.

c. Do not select 2 answers. Marking more than one answer will result in zero score for the question.

d. It is very useful for you to have your own notes written on this book when you study. You may draw some sketches, put some additional explanations or even add some questions. These notes will be helpful later if you go back and review the materials again.

4. After answering all of the questions, use the correct answers to count your score. Your score must be above 75% in order to pass. The answer key is at the end of the book.

5. After identifying the incorrect answers, you need to go back to the materials you studied and ensure you have the correct understanding of the topic.

6. It is very useful to redo the question bank but after you keep it aside for a while (maybe a week).

The icon ⌇ at the end of same questions refers to challenging questions.

Good luck,
Ali M. Al-Shurafa

Category 1 Body of Knowledge

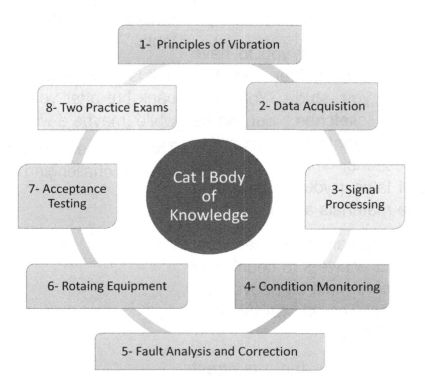

CAT I PART 1 BODY OF KNOWLEDGE

Below is the Body of Knowledge (BoK) as specified by ISO 18436-2 for Part 1 "Principles of Vibration". For a complete list of topics, refer to Part 8 or the Standard.

Topic	Details
Basic motion	Recognize vibration and understand the origin of the sine wave.
Period, frequency	Recognize the following features of a vibration signal: time axis, period, frequency. Use of hertz or cycles per minute
Amplitude (peak, peak-topeak, r.m.s.)	Recognize the following features of a vibration signal: amplitude, peak, peak-to-peak, r.m.s.
Parameters (displacement, velocity, acceleration)	Recognize the following parameters: displacement, velocity, and acceleration
Units, unit conversions	Recognize that units conversion is possible
Time and frequency domains	Be aware of time and frequency domain
Natural frequency, resonance, critical speeds	Be aware resonance exists, and its effect on vibration

FORMULA SHEET FOR CAT I PREP I PART I

<u>Constants:</u>

1 Hz = 1 cps = 60 cpm = 60 rpm

1 minute = 60 seconds = 60,000 milliseconds

$\pi \approx 3.14$ 1 rad/sec $\approx$ 9.55 cpm $g \approx 386.1 \text{ in/sec}^2 \approx 9.81 \text{ m/s}^2$

<u>Equations:</u>

$$\text{Order } nx = \frac{F}{\text{Speed}} \qquad F = \frac{\text{Cycles}}{T} \qquad P = \frac{1}{f}$$

Order = Unitless (ratio)   F = Frequency of vibration (cpm)

Speed = Shaft rotational frequency (rpm)

T = Time covered (sec)   Cycles = Count of cycles captured over time T

P = Period (sec) for a single complete cycle

f = Frequency (Hz)

Simplified General Motion Equation

$$m * a + c * v + k * d = f(t)$$

m = mass (lbm),   c = damping (lb.sec/in)   k = stiffness (lb/in)
a = acceleration (g)   v = velocity (ips)   d = displacement (mil)
f(t) = force function of time (lbf)

Units shown above are for reference only and should not be used for the general motion equation.

Amplitude conversions for a single frequency in Hz

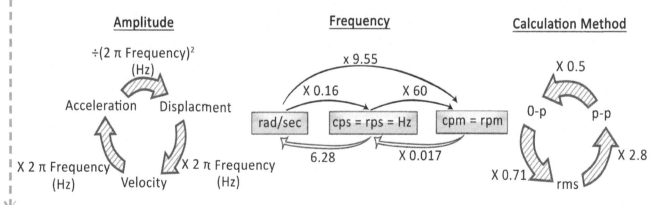

FORMULA SHEET FOR CAT I PREP I PART I

Vibration Amplitude =

Value + Unit (mil / ips / G) + Method (rms / 0-p / p-p) +Frequency (Overall/ Filtered)

Example amplitudes for a signal at 30 Hz (1800 cpm, 30 cps, 188 rad/sec)

	mil	um	ips	mmps	g
rms	2.1	54	0.4	10.2	0.2
0-p	3	76	0.57	14.4	0.28
p-p	6	152	1.13	28.7	0.55

Notes

QUESTION BANK

MORE THAN
120
Questions
PART
1
2019

PRINCIPLES OF VIBRATION

Ali M. Al-Shurafa

Principles of Vibration
Question 001

What is true about mechanical vibration of an object?

A. It is a cyclic motion.

B. It is the cause of rotor unbalance and shaft misalignment.

C. It is a property of the machine that stores energy.

D. It is the variation in gap voltage of an accelerometer mounted on a bearing housing.

Note : ....

....

....

What are the vibration tests that a senior vibration analyst typically conducts or should be able to conduct for rotating equipment?

A. Periodic monitoring and baseline establishment

B. Condition evaluation and fault diagnosis

C. Acceptance and design testing

D. All of the above

Note : ....

....

....

Principles of Vibration
Question 003

A main objective of vibration analysis is to determine the faults or the sources of vibratory forces. What are examples of common vibratory forces in machinery?

A. Cavitation, surge, ski slop and 90 degree phase

B. Sidebands, filtered vibration, crest factor and circular orbit

C. Unbalance, misalignment, looseness and background vibration

D. A & B

Note : ....
....
....

Principles of Vibration
Question **004**

1 mil = 1/1000 inch and 1 micron = 1/1000 mm. In practice, vibration measurement is more accurate using mils compared to microns. That is why mils are preferred. True or False?

A. True, because a micron is larger than a mil.

B. True, because the sensors measuring mils are more accurate.

C. False, both units represent the same physical quantity, despite the difference in the values.

D. False, comparison is impossible between mil and micron without knowing the vibration frequency.

Note : ....

....

....

Principles of Vibration
Question 005

What do the following represent? Order, Hz and CPM.

A. Common methods to measure vibration amplitude.

B. Famous brand names for vibration analysis products.

C. Units for vibration frequency.

D. None of the above.

Note : ....

....

....

Which set of the following are the most common amplitude units used for industrial machinery vibration?

A.	degree	Vol	dB
B.	inch/sec (mm/sec)	G	mile (km)
C.	ft (m)	ft/sec (m/sec)	ft/sec^2 (m/sec^2)
D.	g	mil (µm)	inch/sec (mm/sec)

Note : ....

....

....

Principles of Vibration
Question 007

How to find the amplitude and period of a simple vibration signal?
Hint: Draw a sine wave.

	Amplitude	Period
A.	Time between two peaks	Max to min signal values in x-axis
B.	Divide peak by π	Multiply peak by π
C.	Multiply peak by π	Divide peak by π
D.	Max to min signal values in y-axis	Time between two peaks

Note : ....

....

....

What are the typical units used for the following parameters in the field of machinery vibration analysis? SI units are provided in brackets.

	Vibration Force	Time	Vibration Period
A.	ips (mm/sec)	hr	msec
B.	lb (N)	msec	cps
C.	lb (N)	sec	msec
D.	rms	sec	sec

Note : ....

....

....

Principles of Vibration
Question 009

What are the typical units used for the following parameters in the field of machinery vibration analysis? SI units are provided in brackets.

	Displacement	Velocity	Acceleration
A.	mil (μm)	cpm	in/sec² (mm/sec²)
B.	mile (km)	in/sec (mm/sec)	in/sec³ (mm/sec³)
C.	mil (μm)	in/sec (mm/sec)	g
D.	Hz	in/sec (mm/sec)	g

Note : ....

....

....

What could be a descriptor term for each of the next vibration (time waveform) signals?

	1	2	3
A.	Impulse	Gradual	Sinusoidal
B.	Random	Shock	Harmonic
C.	Hybrid	Analogue	Digital
D.	Harmonic	Noise	Filtered

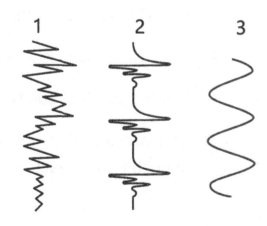

Note : ....

....

....

Principles of Vibration
Question 011

What is true about a sinusoidal signal? Hint : y = A sin (x).

A. It is a signal whose shape is triangular.

B. It is a signal whose shape is rectangular.

C. It is a signal that can be produced using a sine function.

D. It is a signal that has two components with the same frequency imposed over each other.

Note : ....

....

....

In the field of machinery vibration, what does CPS stand for? CPM?

	CPS	CPM
A.	Cage pass spectrum	Case pass monitoring
B.	Complex partial sound	Complex partial measurement
C.	German units	German units
D.	Cycle per second	Cycle per minute

Note : ....

....

....

Principles of Vibration
Question 013

What is the relationship between cpm and cps? Hint: cps = Hz

A. 1 cpm = 60 cps

B. 1 cps = 60 cpm

C. 1 cps < 1 cpm

D. 1 cps = π * cpm

Note : ....

....

....

Principles of Vibration
Question 014

What are the relationships between the following engineering units?

	Hz and cps	Volt & mVolt
A.	60 Hz = 1 cps	1 Volt = 1000 mVolt
B.	1 Hz = 1 cps	1000 Volt = 1 mVolt
C.	1 Hz = 1 cps	1 Volt = 1000 mVolt
D.	1 Hz = 60 cps	1000 Volt = 1 mVolt

Note : ....

....

....

Principles of Vibration
Question 015

Convert the frequency of following vibration signals (A & B) from Hz to cpm.

	Signal A is at 1 Hz	Signal B is at 60 Hz
A.	3600 cpm	60 cpm
B.	60 cpm	3600 cpm
C.	1/60 cpm	1 cpm
D.	10X cpm	1X cpm

Note : ....

....

....

Principles of Vibration
Question **016**

Which equation is used to convert a vibration frequency from cpm to rad/sec? The symbol ≈ means approximately equal.

A. 1 cpm ≈ 3.14 rad/sec

B. 1 cpm ≈ 60 rad/sec

C. 1 cpm ≈ 2.56 rad/ sec

D. 9.55 cpm ≈ 1 rad/sec

Note : ....

....

....

Principles of Vibration
Question 017

If a sound is described as "acute, sharp or high pitch", what type of frequency does it have?

A. Very low

B. Low

C. High

D. A and B

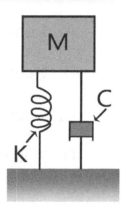

Note :

What are the typical units for the following parameters in the field of machinery vibration analysis? Refer to the illustration. SI units are provided in brackets.

	Stiffness	Shaft Speed
A.	lb/in (N/m)	rpm
B.	lb/in² (N/m²)	rpc
C.	lb/in² (N/m²)	ft/hr (m/sec)
D.	in/lb (m/N)	rpm

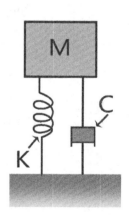

Note : ....

....

....

Principles of Vibration
Question 019

What are the typical units used for the following parameters in the field of machinery vibration analysis? Refer to the illustration.

	Weight	Mass	Damping
A.	lb (N)	lbm (kg)	lb*sec/in (kg*sec/m)
B.	ips (mm/sec)	lbm (kg)	lb/in (N/m)
C.	G	cpm	lb*in*sec (kg*m*sec)
D.	lb (N)	in/sec² (m/sec²)	in/lb*sec (m/N*sec)

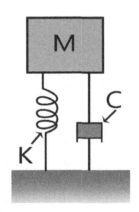

How many degrees are in the following cases: a complete shaft rotation, half a turn and quarter of a turn? Refer to the sketch.

	Turn	Half a Turn	Quarter of a Turn
A.	π°	π /2°	π /4°
B.	360°	180°	90°
C.	rad°	rad/2°	rad/4°
D.	None of the above		

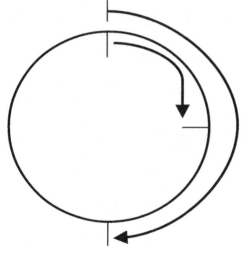

Note : ....

....

....

Principles of Vibration
Question 021

What are other terms used for a "vibration sensor"?

A. Analyzer, data collector and vibration meter

B. Vibration sensing element, probe and vibration transducer

C. Digitizer, discretizer and rectifier

D. A and B

Note : ....

....

....

What is another term used for "casing vibration measurement"? Refer to the illustration.

A. Relative reading

B. Proximity reading

C. Seismic reading

D. Eddy current reading

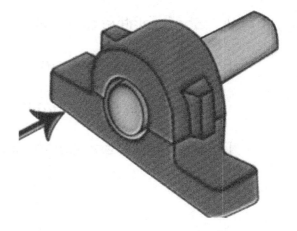

Note : ....

....

....

Principles of Vibration
Question 023

What are other terms commonly used for "shaft vibration"? Refer to the illustration.

A. Shaft relative and case absolute readings

B. Eddy current and proximity readings

C. Seismic and acceleration readings

D. Modulation and demodulation readings

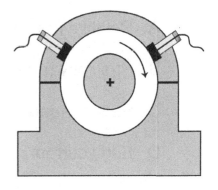

Note : ....

....

....

What is true about "case axial vibration" for a rotating machine?

A. It is a vibration type related to the rotational motion of the shaft.

B. It is another term for lateral vibration.

C. It is a vibration (measured from the bearing house whose direction is along the shaft's axis.

D. It is a vibration measured using an instrumented torque wrench.

Note : ....

....

....

Principles of Vibration
Question 025

What is true about "shaft axial position" for rotating equipment?

A. It is a vibration type related to the rotational motion of the shaft.

B. It is another term for lateral vibration. This parameter is critical for seals.

C. It is a case vibration whose direction is in the shaft's axis.

D. It is a relative distance between the shaft and the equipment's case in the axial direction. This parameter is critical for thrust bearings.

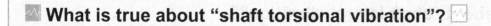 **What is true about "shaft torsional vibration"?**

A. It is another term for speed fluctuation.

B. It is another term for shaft radial vibration.

C. It is a vibration related to relative twisting between points along the shaft axis.

D. It is a vibration measured using an instrumented torque wrench.

Note : ....

....

....

Principles of Vibration
Question 027

What is true about "shaft lateral vibration"?

A. It is a vibration type related to the axial motion of the shaft.

B. It is another term for shaft radial vibration.

C. It is a vibration amplitude that is above the shutdown set point.

D. It is a vibration taking place after equipment start up. Also, it's referred to as longitudinal vibration.

Note : ....

....

....

Which of the following plots is a vibration frequency spectrum?

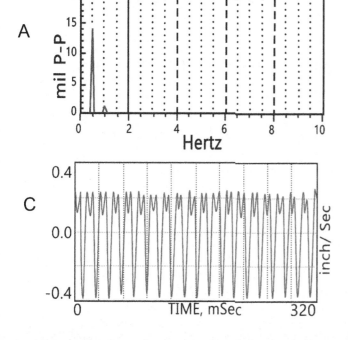

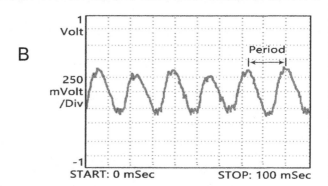

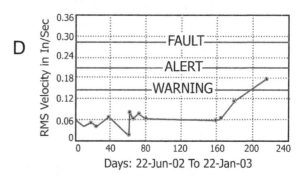

Principles of Vibration
Question 029

What does a waveform plot/data represent in the field of machinery vibration? It represents _____.

A. the physical motion of the measured object along the axis of the sensor.

B. the original data (prior to signal processing) from which other plots are generated.

C. two-dimensional (2D) motion of the shaft inside the bearing clearance viewed from the axial direction.

D. A and B.

Note : ....

....

....

> **For a classic vibration waveform collected from a bearing housing, what is the variable in x-axis, y-axis and their typical units?**

	X-axis (unit)	Y-axis (unit)
A.	Amplitude (inch/sec or mm/s)	Amplitude (cpm)
B.	Amplitude (inch/sec or mm/s)	Frequency (Hz)
C.	Time (msec)	Amplitude (inch/sec or mm/s)
D.	Time (minutes)	Amplitude (ips or mm/s)

Note : ....

....

....

Principles of Vibration
Question 031

For a typical overall vibration trend, what is the variable in the x-axis and its units?

	X-axis Variable	Unit
A.	Frequency	cps, cpm or Hz
B.	Time	sec , min, hr or day
C.	Velocity	mil (μm), ips (mm/s) or g
D.	Amplitude	mil (μm), ips (mm/s) or g

Note : ....

....

....

Assume you monitor vibration on a large pump with journal bearings. For a typical overall vibration trend, what is the variable in the y-axis and its unit?

	Y-axis Variable	Unit
A.	Amplitude	mil (μm)
B.	Frequency	cpm or Hz
C.	Speed	rpm
D.	Phase	deg or part of rotation

Note : ....

....

....

Principles of Vibration
Question 033

What are the three (3) most common/useful vibration plots used for machinery vibration analysis?

A. Shaft average centerline, normal spectrum and full spectrum

B. Trend, spectrum and waveform

C. Cascade, waterfall and Bode plot

D. Polar, 1X trend and gap voltage trend

Note : ....

....

....

For basic machinery vibration analysis, which type of the following plots can be considered the most commonly used (useful) plot in industry?

A. Waveform

B. Spectrum

C. Bode Plot

D. Gap Voltage Trend

Note : ....

....

....

Principles of Vibration
Question 035

Which plot type can be considered as the origin of the other vibration plots?

A. Gap Voltage Trend

B. Waveform

C. Full Spectrum

D. Bode Plot

Note : ....

....

....

Which plots provide vibration data in a form of vibration level (y-axis) versus time (x-axis)?

A. Spectrum and 1X Trend

B. Bode and Spectrum

C. Overall Trend and Waveform

D. Orbit and RMS Algorithm

Note : ....

....

....

Principles of Vibration
Question 037

Which of the following is a sine signal?

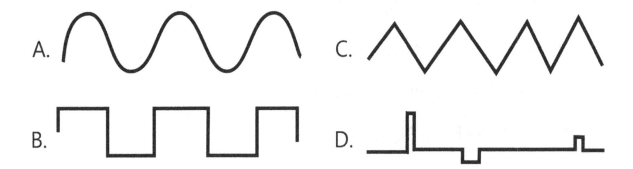

A.

B.

C.

D.

Note : ....

....

....

A vibration signal is added to another vibration signal. Both signals have the same frequency, amplitude and phase. What is the resultant signal? Refer to the next illustration.

A. Double frequency signal

B. Double amplitude signal

C. Double phase signal

D. All of the above.

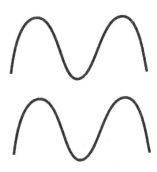

Note : ....

....

....

Principles of Vibration
Question 039

Which of the following waveforms has a high amplitude and a high frequency? Assume all plots share the same scales.

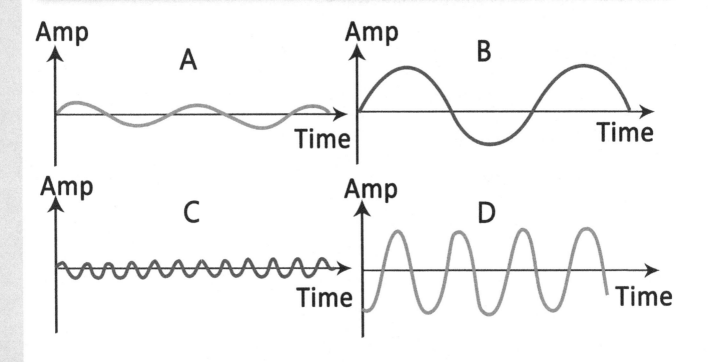

Which of the following waveforms has a low amplitude and short period? Assume all plots share the same scales.

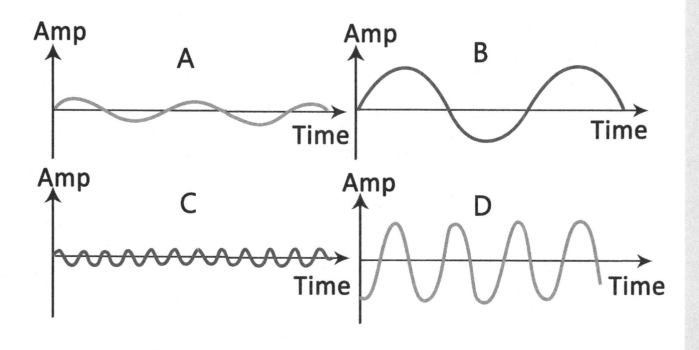

Principles of Vibration
Question 041

What kind of vibration plot is in the next illustration? It is taken from a large pump. X-axis is in msec. Y-axis is in mils.

A. Overall trend

B. Gap voltage trend

C. Waveform without a key phasor

D. Filtered waveform with a key phasor

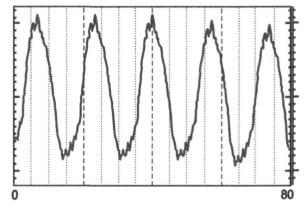

Note : ....

....

....

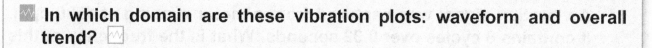 **In which domain are these vibration plots: waveform and overall trend?**

A. Frequency domain

B. Time domain

C. Phase domain

D. Amplitude domain

Note :

Principles of Vibration
Question 043

A vibration signal was captured from a motor running at 1500 cpm. It contains 8 cycles over 0.32 seconds. What is the frequency of this signal? Hint: Draw the signal.

A. 2.56 Hz

B. 0.04 Hz

C. 187.5 Hz

D. 25 Hz

Note : ....

....

....

Principles of Vibration
Question 044

If a shaft vibrates up and down 3595 times in a minute, what is the frequency of this vibration?

A. 3595 Hz

B. 3595 cpm

C. 3595 cps

D. 59.5 cpm

Note : ....

....

....

Principles of Vibration
Question 045

What is the frequency and the period of the following vibration signal?

	Frequency	Period
A.	0.1 ips	0.1 msec
B.	0.1 sec	0.1 msec
C.	10 Hz	0.1 sec
D.	None of the above.	

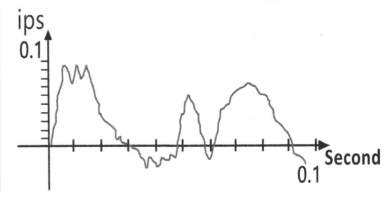

Note : ....

....

....

Refer to the next plot. What is the frequency in cpm and rad/sec? Expect some rounding.

	cpm	rad/sec
A.	1333	140
B.	22.2	1364
C.	22.2	143
D.	2985	312

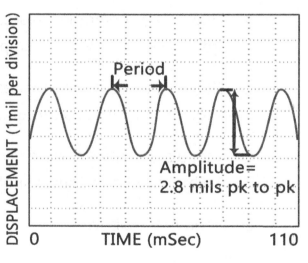

Note :

Principles of Vibration
Question 047

What do the following represent in the field of machinery vibration analysis? 1x TS, 1 x SS, 1x STS and 1x rpm.

A. These are common expressions used for machinery vibration amplitude. A vibration amplitude equals shaft rotational speed.

B. These are common expressions used for machinery vibration frequency. A vibration frequency equals the shaft rotational speed.

C. These are common expressions used for machinery vibration phase. A vibration phase equals shaft rotational speed.

D. None of the above.

Note : ....

....

....

〰 **How much time (in seconds) does a shaft need to rotate a full turn if its speed is 600 rpm, 3590 rpm and 52000 rpm? Refer to the illustration. Hint: convert rpm to Hz. Expect some rounding.**

	600 rpm	3590 rpm	52000 rpm
A.	0.00167	0.0003	0.00002
B.	0.1	0.0167	0.0012
C.	10	16.7	1.15
D.	None of the above		

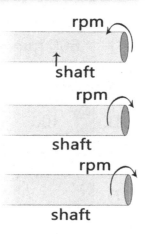

Note : ....

....

....

Principles of Vibration
Question 049

> How much time (in mseconds) does a shaft need to rotate a full turn if its speed is 600 rpm, 3590 rpm and 52000 rpm? Refer to the illustration.
> Hint: 1 sec = 1000 msec

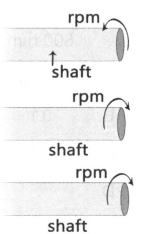

	600 rpm	3590 rpm	52000 rpm
A.	0.00167	0.0003	0.00002
B.	100	16.7	1.2
C.	10	59.8	867
D.	None of the above		

rpm
shaft

rpm
shaft

rpm
shaft

Note : ....

....

....

Principles of Vibration
Question 050

A vibration signal of 0.01 inch per second p-p at 10 Hz will repeat itself every:_____.

A. 0.1 sec

B. 1 sec

C. 10 sec

D. 100 sec

Note : ....

....

....

Principles of Vibration
Question 051

A vibration signal of 10 mm/sec 0-p at 0.1 Hz will repeat itself every:_____.

A. 0.1 sec

B. 1 sec

C. 10 sec

D. 100 sec

Note : ....

....

....

The period of a simple vibration signal is 0.01 second. The phase of 1X is 1 deg. What is its frequency and amplitude for this signal? Hint: Draw the signal.

	Frequency	Amplitude
A.	0.01 cps	$1°$
B.	100 cycles per second	1 %
C.	1 cpm	0.01 %
D.	100 Hz	Cannot be found based on the provided information.

Note : ....

....

....

Question 053

A shaft vibration signal of 120 µm p-p takes 0.06 seconds to develop a complete cycle. The scale factor of the sensor is unknown. What is the frequency of this signal in cps and rad/sec? Expect same rounding. Hint: 1 rad/sec ≈ 9.55 cpm

	cps	rad/sec
A.	20	1047
B.	200	1000
C.	16.7	104.7
D.	16.7	1002

Note : ....

....

....

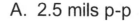 **Study the next waveform. The instrument's scale factor is 200 mV/mil. What is the amplitude? Hint: scale factor is used to convert voltage readings to vibration readings. First, find the amplitude from the plot in volt.**

A. 2.5 mils p-p

B. 5 mils p-p

C. 5 mils 0-p

D. 10 mils p-p

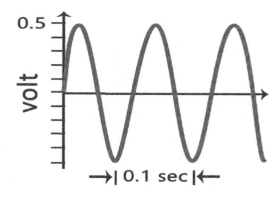

Note : ....
....
....

Principles of Vibration
Question 055

A vibration signal repeats itself every 4.5 msec. What is the frequency in Hz? What is the period? Expect some rounding.

	Frequency (Hz)	Period (sec)
A.	222	0.0045
B.	0.22	4500
C.	4500	0.22
D.	4.5	0.0045

Note : ....

....

....

A vibration signal of 0.005 inch p-p takes 0.06 seconds to develop a cycle. The scale factor of the used sensor is 0.1 V/mil. What is the vibration frequency of this signal in Hz? What is the amplitude? Phase? Expect some rounding.

	Hz	Amplitude	Phase
A.	200	0.005 mil p-p	60 msec
B.	20	6 mil p-p	0
C.	16.7	50 mil p-p	0.1 V/mil
D.	16.7	5 mil p-p	Unknown

Note : ....

....

....

Principles of Vibration
Question 057

For the next plot, what is the amplitude in mils (0-p, p-p and rms)?

	0-P	P-P	RMS
A.	5	10	3.5
B.	5	10	7.07
C.	3.5	5	10
D.	10	5	3.5

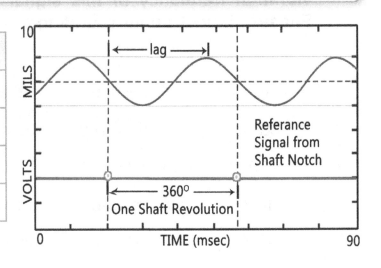

Note : ....

....

....

Study the next plot. What is the frequency in cpm, cps, rad/sec and Hz? Expect some rounding.

	cpm	cps	rad/sec	Hz
A.	1622	217	170	217
B.	15	900	250	1570
C.	1579	26.3	165	26.3
D.	8570	143	898	143

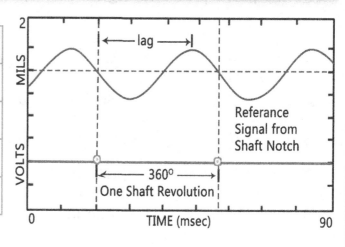

Note : ....

....

....

Principles of Vibration
Question 059

A vibration signal of 0.007 mm p-p takes 0.08 seconds to develop a complete cycle. The data acquisition time is 0.56 sec. What is the frequency of this signal in Hz, cpm and order? What is the period?

	Hz	cpm	order	Period
A.	12.5	750	Unknown	80 msec
B.	750	45000	Unknown	80 msec
C.	143	560	1X	8 msec
D.	560	11.4 sec/mm	2X	60 mil p-p

Note : ....

....

....

A vibration signal of 0.005 inch p-p takes 0.06 seconds to develop a cycle. The scale factor of the used sensor is 0.1 V/mil. What is true about this signal?

A. The signal is a simple displacement wave whose period is 6 msec.

B. This is a simple wave whose amplitude is 5 mil p-p.

C. The frequency of this signal is 16.6 Hz or 1000 cpm.

D. B and C.

Note : ....

....

....

Principles of Vibration
Question 061

A vibration signal of 0.007 mm p-p takes 0.08 seconds to develop a cycle. The data acquisition time is 0.56 sec. What is the amplitude, period and Phase?

	Amplitude	Period	Phase
A.	7 µm p-p	80 msec	Unknown
B.	7 mm p-p	80 msec	0
C.	0.007 µm p-p	8 msec	0.1 V/mil
D.	80 msec	7 mil p-p	560 msec

Note : ....

....

....

Knowing 1.0 inch ≈ 25.4 mm, convert these two vibration amplitudes from mm/sec to inch/sec. Expect some rounding.

	5 mm/sec 0-p at 30 Hz	5 mm/sec 0-p at 60 Hz
A.	0.2 ips 0-p	0.4 ips 0-p
B.	0.2 ips 0-p	0.2 ips 0-p
C.	5 ips 0-p	5 ips 0-p
D.	13 ips 0-p	26 ips 0-p

Note : ....

....

....

Principles of Vibration
Question 063

For the next plot, what is the amplitude in mils (0-P, P-P and RMS)?

	0-P	P-P	RMS
A.	1	2	0.707
B.	2	1	1.414
C.	180°	360°	270°
D.	30°	38°	18°

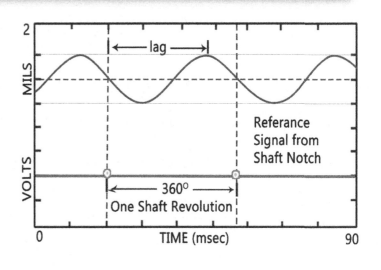

Note : ....

....

....

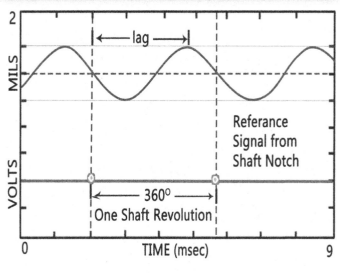 **Study the next plot. What is the frequency in cpm and order? Expect some rounding.**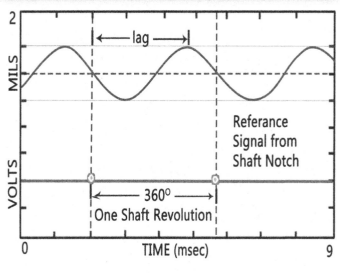

	cpm	Order
A.	8	3.8X
B.	15.8	2.9X
C.	1579	1X
D.	16216	9X

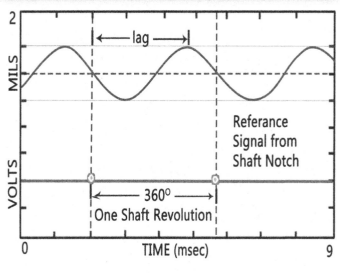

Referance Signal from Shaft Notch

360° One Shaft Revolution

TIME (msec)

lag

MILS

VOLTS

Note : ....

....

....

Principles of Vibration
Question 065

Refer to the next plot. What is the period in milliseconds and seconds? How much time is needed to develop 8 cycles? Expect some rounding.

	P (msec)	P (sec)	8 Cycles (sec)
A.	5	0.005	0.1
B.	0.022	0.002	0.016
C.	22	0.022	0.176
D.	0.2	0.20	0.16

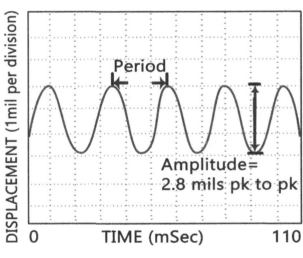

Note : ....

....

....

Refer to the next plot. What is the frequency in Hz and cps? Expect some rounding.

	Hz	cps
A.	0.04545	0.04545
B.	45.45	45.45
C.	50	500
D.	100	50

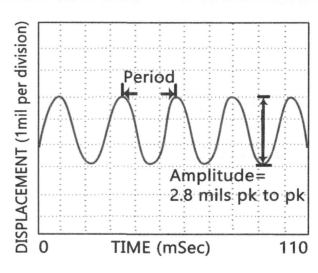

Note : ....

....

....

Principles of Vibration
Question 067

Study the next waveforms and spectra. Which plots are related?

A. 1 and 3

B. 1 and 4

C. 2 and 3

D. 2 and 4

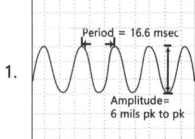
1.

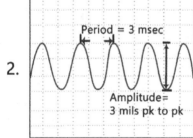
2.

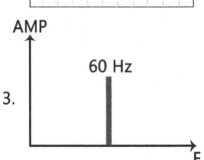
3.

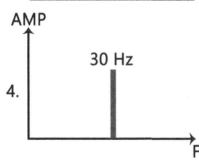
4.

Study the next vibration waveform and spectra. Which spectrum is related the waveform? Y-axis is in mils.

A. 1 and 2

B. 2 and 3

C. 1 and 3

D. Only 2

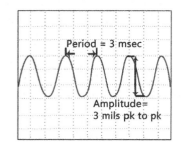

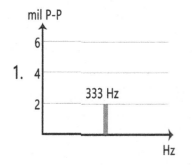

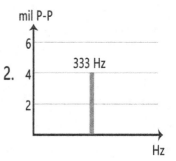

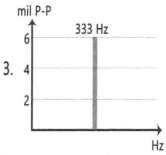

Principles of Vibration
Question 069

Which of the following represents a vibration waveform signal whose amplitude is 10 mils p-p at 30 Hz? Expect some rounding.

A.
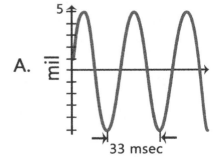

B.
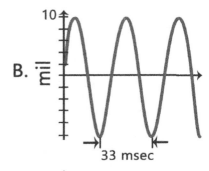

C.
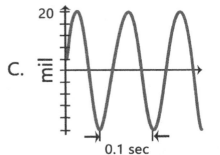

D.
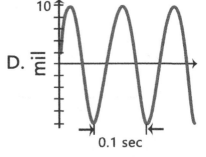

Which of the following represents a vibration waveform signal whose amplitude is 10 mm/sec 0-p at 59 Hz? Expect some rounding.

A.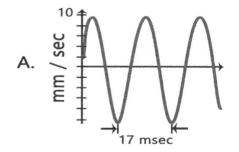

B.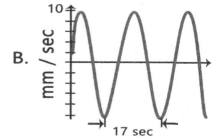

C.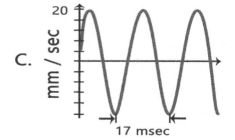

D.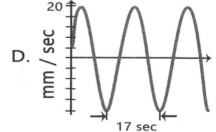

Which of the following represents a vibration waveform signal whose amplitude is 2.59 mm/sec 0-p at 3530 cpm? Expect some rounding.

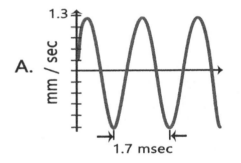

A.

1.3

mm / sec

1.7 msec

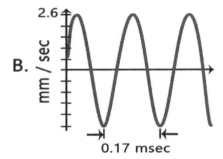

B.

2.6

mm / sec

0.17 msec

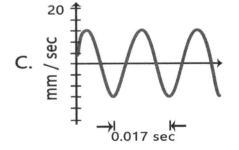

C.

20

mm / sec

0.017 sec

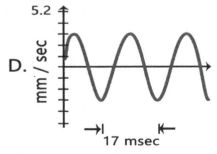

D.

5.2

mm / sec

17 msec

The scale factor is 0.1 V/mil for the next waveform. What is the amplitude? What is the period? Hint: vib (mil) = vib (volt) ÷ Scale factor (V/mil).

	Amplitude	Period
A.	0.2 mils p-p	100 msec
B.	10 mils 0-p	200 msec
C.	24 mils p-p	100 msec
D.	3 mils 0-p	0.100 sec

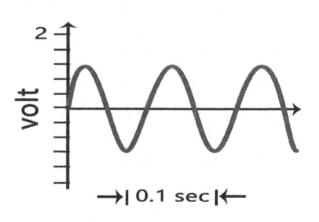

Note : ....

....

....

Principles of Vibration
Question 073

Study the provided vibration plot. What is the value of: data acquisition time, positive peak and negative peak? Expect some rounding.

	DAT	+Peak	-Peak
A.	0.1 sec	0.3 ips	-0.25 ips
B.	100 msec	357 mV	-357 mV
C.	100 sec	1 Volt	-1 Volt
D.	0.017 sec	1.5 V	-1.5 V

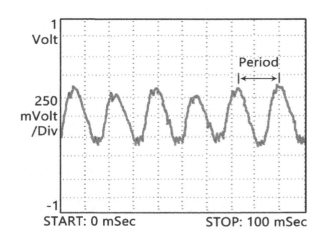

Note : ....

....

....

Study the provided vibration plot. What is the value of period? What is the frequency of the dominant signal? Some answers are approximated.

	Period	Frequency
A.	16.7 sec	60 cpm
B.	16.7 msec	0.32 sec
C.	16.7 msec	60 Hz
D.	19 msec	66 Hz

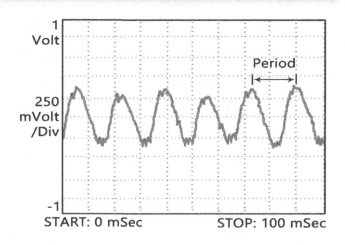

Note : ....

....

....

Principles of Vibration
Question 075

Study this vibration plot. What are the following parameters: main frequency, positive peak, negative peak? Expect some rounding.

	Frequency	+ Peak	- Peak
A.	16.7 second	0.21 mil	-0.39 mil
B.	3565 cpm	0.4 inch/ sec	-0.4 inch/ sec
C.	60 Hz	0.22 ips	-0.38 ips
D.	16.7 msec	0.6 ips	-320 msec

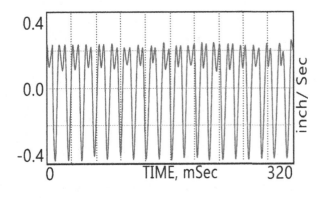

🗠 **Study this vibration plot. What are following parameters? Expect some rounding.**

	Period	Dominant Frequency
A.	16.6 sec	60 cpm
B.	16.6 msec	0.32 cps
C.	16.6 msec	3592 cpm
D.	19 msec	320 Hz

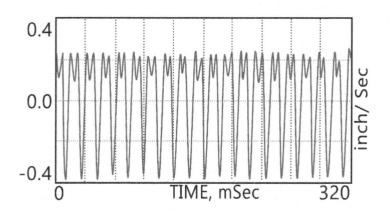

Note : ....

....

....

Principles of Vibration
Question 077

Refer to the next plot. What is the data acquisition time and the overall amplitude in ips 0-p? How much time is needed to develop 8 cycles? Expect some rounding.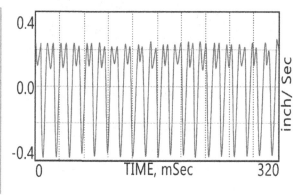

	DAT	Amplitude	8 Cycles
A.	0.7 Sec	-0.40	30.4 msec
B.	320 msec	0.38	134 msec
C.	0.32 sec	0.22	192 msec
D.	16.7 msec	0.28	320 msec

Note : ....

....

....

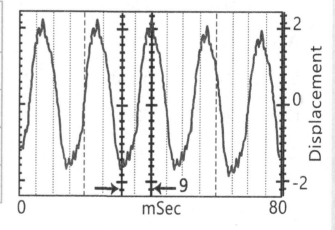 **Study the next plot. What is the data collection time and the period? How much time is needed to develop 8 cycles? Expect some rounding.**

	DAT (msec)	P (sec)	8 Cycles (sec)
A.	4	0.08	0.064
B.	18	16	0.080
C.	16	0.08	0.800
D.	80	0.016	0.128

Note : ....

....

....

Question 079

Refer to the next plot. What is the dominant frequency in Hz, cpm and rad/sec? Expect some rounding.

	Hz	cpm	rad/sec
A.	42	2500	262
B.	84	5040	1605
C.	21	1260	132
D.	12	720	75

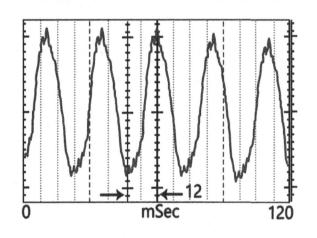

Note : ....

....

....

What is the period for the major component? How much time is needed to develop 8 vibration cycles? Refer to the next plot. Expect some rounding.

	P	8 Cycles
A.	0.5 msec	4 msec
B.	200 msec	1.6 sec
C.	0.5 sec	20 sec
D.	2 sec	16 sec

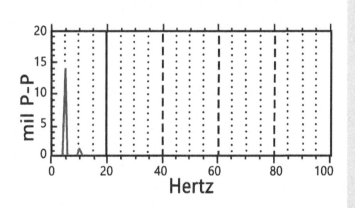

Note : ....

....

....

Principles of Vibration
Question 081

Assume you monitor a vibration signal on a screen of an analyzer. What will happen to the resultant vibration signal if the sensor's scale factor is changed?

A. Phase will change.

B. Amplitude will change.

C. Frequency will change.

D. Period will change.

Note : ....

....

....

Assume you monitor a simple vibration signal on a screen of an analyzer. What will happen to the resultant vibration signal if you increase data collection time?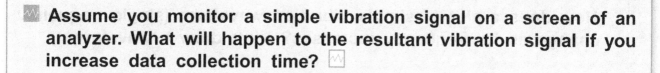

A. Amplitude of the vibration signal will decrease.

B. Frequency of the vibration signal will increase.

C. Period of the vibration signal will increase.

D. None of the above

Note : ....

....

....

Principles of Vibration
Question 083

> How does a plot of simple vibration waveform (single frequency) change as its frequency increases? Hint: draw a waveform.

A. Less number of cycles are captured over the same time frame.

B. More number of cycles are captured over the same time frame.

C. The time required to collect a single complete cycle increases.

D. The period of the signal increases.

Note : ....

....

....

Principles of Vibration
Question 084

What happens to a vibration waveform when the vibration signal includes more frequencies? Usually, its_____.

A. shape becomes smoother

B. shape becomes complex

C. amplitude significantly increases

D. amplitude significantly decreases

Note : ....

....

....

Principles of Vibration
Question 085

How does a plot of a simple vibration waveform (single frequency) change as its period increases?

A. The time required to collect a single complete cycle decreases.

B. The frequency of the signal increases.

C. Less number of cycles are captured over the same time frame.

D. More number of cycles are captured over the same time frame.

Note : ....
....
....

Principles of Vibration
Question 086

 How does a simple vibration waveform (single frequency) change as its amplitude increases? Example: from 0.3 ips 0-P to 0.5 ips 0-P.

A. The positive peak value (y-axis) increases.

B. The positive peak value (x-axis) decreases.

C. The phase angle increases.

D. The frequency decreases.

Note : ....

....

....

Principles of Vibration
Question 087

Consider typical industrial vibration applications. Which measurement is the best to represent each of the following dynamic parameters?

	Movement of Tall Structures (1 - 100 Hz)	Rotor Vibration in a Journal Bearing (1- 1000 Hz)
A.	Velocity	Velocity
B.	Acceleration	Velocity
C.	Displacement	Acceleration
D.	Displacement	Displacement

Note : ....

....

....

Consider typical industrial vibration applications like machines at speed between 20- 60 Hz. Which measurement is the best to represent each of the following dynamic parameters?

	Fatigue of a Mechanical Component	Exciting Forces
A.	Displacement	Displacement
B.	Velocity	Velocity
C.	Displacement	Acceleration
D.	Velocity	Acceleration

Note : ....

....

....

Principles of Vibration
Question 089

What is the famous equation (simplified) for Newton's second law of motion? Hint: This equation relates vibration to excitation.

A. Force = Mass ÷ Acceleration

B. Force = Mass x Acceleration

C. Hertz = Cycle per second x 60

D. Pressure = Area ÷ Force

Note : ....

....

....

For real industrial machines, how common is it for a shaft to deflect (sag) because of the weight of an impeller mounted on it? Refer to the illustration.

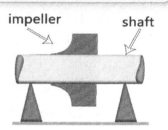

impeller   shaft

A. This case never happens. Industrial shafts can carry the weight of heavy impellers.

B. It happens if distance between bearings is large compared to the diameter of the rotor. Or, it happens if shaft is kept stationery under the load of a heavy impeller for a long time.

C. The deflection depends directly on the misalignment which needs prevention in the first place.

D. All rotors deflect or sag due to the effect of the monitoring system.

Principles of Vibration
Question 091

What is true about "resonance" in machinery vibration analysis?

A. It is a condition where machine can vibrate severely or easily due to high unbalance forces.

B. It is an excited condition where machine's natural frequency is close to the frequency of the applied force.

C. It is a condition where machine's natural frequency is way greater than the frequency of the applied forces.

D. A and B

Note : ....

....

....

Mechanical systems like a rotating machine can be simplified as a mathematical model of mass, stiffness and_____ . Hint: refer to the sketch.

A. spring

B. damping

C. calibration

D. beat

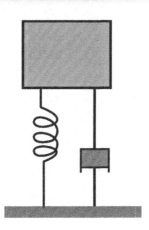

Note :

Principles of Vibration
Question 093

Generally speaking, the natural frequency of a machine depends on its stiffness and _____.

A. mass distribution

B. probe type

C. imbalance frequency order

D. All of the above

Note : ....

....

....

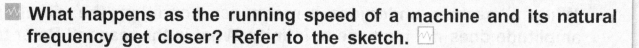 What happens as the running speed of a machine and its natural frequency get closer? Refer to the sketch.

A. Misalignment gets worse.

B. Mass increases.

C. Probability of a higher vibration increases.

D. Spectrum resolution decreases.

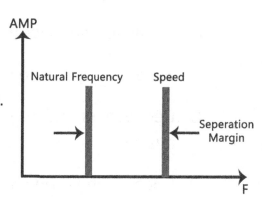

Note : ....

....

....

Principles of Vibration
Question 095

> When a machine undergoes a resonance condition, the vibration amplitude does not increase to infinity. What is the reason? Refer to the sketch.

A. Because resonance usually takes place during equipment installation.

B. Because resonance condition is relatively weak.

C. Because of the presence of damping in the system.

D. Because the online protection system can easily detect resonance at early stages.

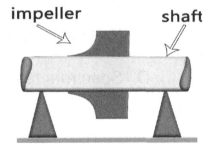

impeller   shaft

Note : ....

....

....

In the field of machinery vibration analysis, what does "in-phase" and "out of phase" mean?
Refer to the sketch.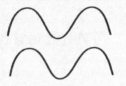

	In-Phase	Out of Phase
A.	Two signals move towards the peak together.	Two signals move in the opposite direction relative to the peak.
B.	Phase angle of both signals is very similar.	Phase angle of both signals is (or almost) opposite.
C.	Amplitudes of both signals are equal.	Amplitudes of both signals are very different.
D.	A and B	

Question 097

What is a typical application of "phase" in practical vibration analysis?

A. To distinguish between similar machinery faults (e.g. misalignment and unbalance).

B. To perform rotor balancing (shop and on site).

C. To analyze transient data (i.e. startup and shutdown).

D. All of the above.

During machinery vibration measurements, under what condition an amplitude in the x-axis can significantly differ from the reading from other axes? Refer to the sketch.

A. If the force acting on the machine is directional (i.e. significantly higher on one direction than other directions).

B. If the structure of the machine is significantly stronger in one direction compared to the other directions.

C. If the vibration transducer is highly sensitive.

D. A and B.

Principles of Vibration
Question 099

Usually three (3) vibration measurements are taken from each bearing housing of a machine. What are they?

A.	Vertical	Horizontal	Axial
B.	Sub-synchronous	Synchronous	Super-synchronous
C.	Displacement	Velocity	Acceleration
D.	B and C		

Principles of Vibration
Question **100**

Consider a simple (filtered) vibration signal from an electric generator. What are the relationships between these methods of amplitude calculation: 0-p, p-p and rms? Hint: sketch a waveform.

A.	1 mil 0-p = 2 mil p-p	1 mil 0-p = 0.707 mil rms
B.	2 mil 0-p = 1 mil p-p	1 mil rms = 0.707 mil 0-p
C.	1 mil rms = 0.707 mil 0-p	2 mil rms = 0.707 mil 0-p
D.	None of the above	

Note : ....

....

....

Principles of Vibration
Question 101

What is true about displacement, velocity and acceleration in the field of machinery vibration?

A. These are the physical variables of vibration amplitude.

B. These are the physical variables of vibration frequency.

C. These are the physical variables in the x- axis of waveforms and spectra

D. The conversion from one to another is impossible.

Note : ....

....

....

In practice, which vibration measure (displacement, velocity and acceleration) uses 0-p, p-p and rms?

	Displacement	Velocity and Acceleration
A.	p-p	0-p and rms
B.	rms	0-p and p-p
C.	0-p and rms	p-p
D.	In practice, all combinations are commonly used and widely acceptable.	

Note : ....

....

....

Principles of Vibration
Question 103

Consider a vibration signal at 60 Hz that is measured in 0-p. The amplitude cannot be converted from 0-p to p-p after the data is collected. True or False?

A. True. Conversion of an amplitude introduces a lot of error (after measurement).

B. True. Conversion of amplitude unit is possible but converting the method of calculation is not possible.

C. False, the relationships between 0-p, p-p and rms always hold true for any vibration signal with a single frequency.

D. False. A frequency at 60 Hz is possible to convert because it is a special case. (Conversion is not possible for other frequencies.)

Consider a vibration signal at 120 Hz measured in mm/sec. The amplitude cannot be converted from mm/sec to in/sec after the data has been collected. True or False?

A. True, specially if amplitude is more than 12.5 mm/sec (or 0.5 ips).

B. True. Single frequency amplitude cannot be converted at 120 Hz. Frequency at 120 Hz is a special case.

C. False, any overall vibration amplitude or a single frequency amplitude can be converted from mm/sec to in/sec (from metric to customary units) and vice versa.

D. The information provided is not enough to make the conversion. Phase lag at 120 Hz is needed.

Principles of Vibration
Question 105

Consider a vibration signal at 50 Hz measured in displacement. The amplitude cannot be converted from displacement to velocity after the data was collected. True or False?

A. True. All amplitudes with a single frequency cannot be converted at 50 Hz (because this is special frequency). This special condition is valid for vibrations at line frequencies 50 Hz and 60 Hz.

B. False, any vibration at a single frequency can be converted from displacement to velocity.

C. False, a signal at 50 Hz is a special case that can be converted. (Conversion is not possible for other frequencies.)

D. It depends on the source of vibration. For example, vibration due to unbalance at 50 Hz can be converted but vibration due to misalignment at 50 Hz cannot.

What is the relationship between the following vibration units? Expect some rounding.

	inch & mil	g & inch/ sec^2
A.	1 inch = 1000 mil	1 g = 9.81 in/sec^2
B.	1 inch = 1000 mil	1 g = 386 in/sec^2
C.	1 inch = 100 mil	386 g = 1 in/sec^2
D.	1000 inch = 1 mil	1 g = 386 in/sec^2

Note : ....

....

....

Principles of Vibration
Question 107

How to convert a filtered vibration amplitude from displacement to velocity?

A. Use this formula: velocity = (2 π * frequency) * displacement.

B. Use this formula: velocity = (2 π * frequency)/ displacement.

C. Use this formula: 1 inch = 1000 mils.

D. Use conversion factor: velocity = 0.707 displacement.

Note : ....

....

....

How to convert a filtered vibration amplitude from velocity to acceleration?

A. Use this formula: acceleration = (velocity*2π) * frequency

B. Use this formula: acceleration = (velocity*2π)/frequency

C. Use FFT algorithm

D. Use FFT conversion factor: acceleration = 0.707 velocity

Note : ....

....

....

Principles of Vibration
Question 109

How to convert a filtered vibration amplitude from velocity to displacement?

A. Use this formula: displacement = velocity * (2 π *frequency)

B. Use this formula: displacement = velocity / (2 π* frequency)

C. Use a window factor of 1.5 for Hanning Window

D. Use conversion factor: displacement = 0.707 velocity

Note : ....

....

....

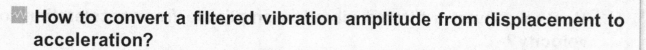 **How to convert a filtered vibration amplitude from displacement to acceleration?**

A. Use this formula: acceleration= displacement * (2 π * frequency)

B. Use this formula: acceleration= displacement * (2 π * frequency)^2

C. Use Hanning window

D. Use FFT conversion factor: acceleration = 0.707 displacement

Note : ....

....

....

Principles of Vibration
Question 111

> ## How to convert a filtered vibration amplitude from acceleration to velocity?

A. Use this formula: velocity = acceleration ÷ (2 π* frequency)

B. Use this formula: acceleration = velocity * 2 π/ frequency

C. Use this formula: $1 \text{ g} = 386 \text{ in/sec}^2$

D. Use FFT acceleration = 0.707 velocity

Note : ....

....

....

Principles of Vibration
Question **112**

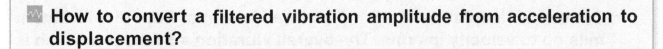

How to convert a filtered vibration amplitude from acceleration to displacement?

A. Conversion is possible only if the acceleration signal is made of three (3) frequencies and more. To convert, add amplitudes.

B. Conversion is possible only from acceleration to velocity.

C. By dividing acceleration value by gravity constant (386.1 in/s^2)

D. Using this formula: displacement = acceleration / (2 π*frequency) ^{2}.

Note : ....

....

....

Question 113

Convert an amplitude of a simple vibration signal from displacement mils pp to velocity ips rms. The overall vibration = 5 mils p-p which is mostly 1X.

A. 0.005 ips rms

B. 0.002 ips rms

C. The given information is not enough to convert.

D. 0.707 ips rms

Note : ....

....

....

Convert 0.33 ips 0-p at 3333 Hz to displacement and acceleration. Given answers may have some rounding.

	Displacement	Acceleration
A	32 mils 0-p	18 g 0-p
B	32 mils p-p	8.95 g 0-p
C	0.032 mils p-p	18 g 0-p
D	More information is needed.	

Note : ....

....

....

Principles of Vibration
Question 115

> Convert 0.44 ips rms at 4444 cpm to displacement and acceleration
> Expect some rounding, on the second decimal digit.

	Displacement	Acceleration
A	2.67 mils p-p	0.75 g 0-p
B	9.5 mil p-p	0.53 g 0-p
C	19.0 mils p-p	0.53 g rms
D	None of the above.	

Note : ....

....

....

Convert 5.55 g rms at 5555 cpm to displacement and velocity. Given answers may have some rounding.

	Displacement	Velocity
A	24 mils p-p	0.37 ips 0-p
B	12 mils p-p	0.175 ips 0-p
C	18 mils p-p	3.7 ips rms
D	None of the above.	

Note : ....

....

....

Principles of Vibration
Question 117

> Convert 6.6 mils p-p at 666 cpm to velocity and acceleration. Given answers may have some rounding.

	Velocity	Acceleration
A	0.12 ips 0-p	0.021 g 0-p
B	0.23 ips 0-p	0.041 g 0-p
C	0.23 ips 0-p	16 g 0-p
D	0.23 ips rms	0.410 g rms

Note : ....

....

....

> **Study the next vibration plot. What is the name of the plot? Highest amplitude? The cause of the vibration?**

	Name	Amplitude	Cause
A.	Spectrum	0.36 ips rms	Unbalance
B.	Trend	0.18 ips rms	Unknown
C.	Waveform	0.18 inch/sec rms	Misalignment
D.	Ultrasound	Unknown	Faulty Signal

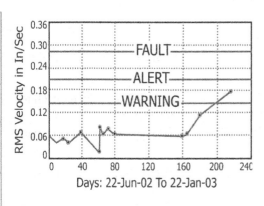

Days: 22-Jun-02 To 22-Jan-03

Note : ....

....

....

Principles of Vibration
Question **119**

Study the next vibration plot. What is the name of the plot? Domain? Natural frequency?

	Name	Domain	Natural Frequency
A.	Spectrum	Frequency	Unknown
B.	Trend	Unknown	10 X
C.	Waveform	Time	1 X
D.	Orbit	Amplitude	14.9 X

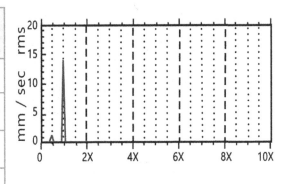

Note : ....

....

....

Refer to the next vibration plot for a small fan. What is the frequency for the highest amplitude in the following units? The speed is 3598 revolutions per minute.

	Hz	cps
A.	30	30
B.	60	60
C.	120	60
D.	0.5 X	1 X

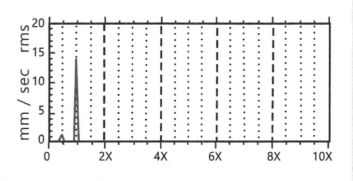

Note : ....

....

....

Principles of Vibration
Question 121

> Refer to the next vibration plot for a small fan. What is the frequency of the second highest amplitude in the following units? The speed is 600 revolutions per minute.

	Hz	cps
A.	300	600
B.	36000	600
C.	20	20
D.	10	10

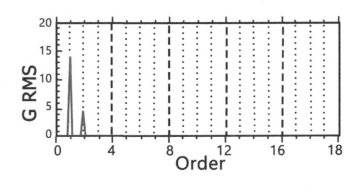

Note : ....

....

....

Refer to the next vibration plot. What is the highest amplitude in the mils peak-to-peak? Based on the provided information, can this component be converted to velocity in ips rms?

A.	7	Yes
B.	14	Yes
C.	28	No
D.	1	No

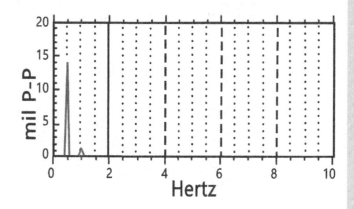

Note : ....

....

....

Principles of Vibration
Question 123

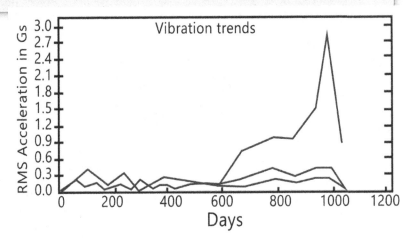 **Study this vibration overall amplitude trend. The plot shows data of x, y and z directions. What is the date and amplitude of the peak value? Plot start date: Jan 20, 2010.**

A.	25 Oct 2012	2.7 g rms
B.	5 Dec 2002	3.3 g rms
C.	20 April 1999	2.7 g 0-p
D.	Jan 20 2018	39 rms

Note : ....

....

....

Study this overall vibration trend. What is the date and amplitude of the peak value?

A.	22 Jun 2002	0.36 ips 0-p
B.	22 Jan 2003	0.13 ips rms
C.	22 Jan 2003	0.18 ips 0-p
D.	None of the above	

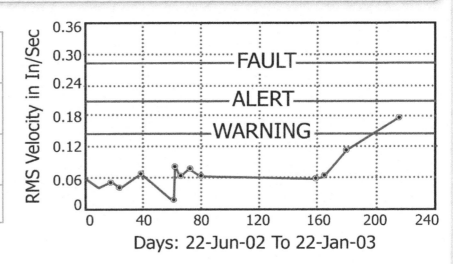

Days: 22-Jun-02 To 22-Jan-03

Note : ....

....

....

ANSWER SHEETS

EMPTY ANSWER SHEET 1

1	A	B	C	D
2	A	B	C	D
3	A	B	C	D
4	A	B	C	D
5	A	B	C	D
6	A	B	C	D
7	A	B	C	D
8	A	B	C	D
9	A	B	C	D
10	A	B	C	D
11	A	B	C	D
12	A	B	C	D
13	A	B	C	D
14	A	B	C	D
15	A	B	C	D

16	A	B	C	D
17	A	B	C	D
18	A	B	C	D
19	A	B	C	D
20	A	B	C	D
21	A	B	C	D
22	A	B	C	D
23	A	B	C	D
24	A	B	C	D
25	A	B	C	D
26	A	B	C	D
27	A	B	C	D
28	A	B	C	D
29	A	B	C	D
30	A	B	C	D

EMPTY ANSWER SHEET 1

31	A	B	C	D
32	A	B	C	D
33	A	B	C	D
34	A	B	C	D
35	A	B	C	D
36	A	B	C	D
37	A	B	C	D
38	A	B	C	D
39	A	B	C	D
40	A	B	C	D
41	A	B	C	D
42	A	B	C	D
43	A	B	C	D
44	A	B	C	D
45	A	B	C	D

46	A	B	C	D
47	A	B	C	D
48	A	B	C	D
49	A	B	C	D
50	A	B	C	D
51	A	B	C	D
52	A	B	C	D
53	A	B	C	D
54	A	B	C	D
55	A	B	C	D
56	A	B	C	D
57	A	B	C	D
58	A	B	C	D
59	A	B	C	D
60	A	B	C	D

EMPTY ANSWER SHEET 1

61	A	B	C	D
62	A	B	C	D
63	A	B	C	D
64	A	B	C	D
65	A	B	C	D
66	A	B	C	D
67	A	B	C	D
68	A	B	C	D
69	A	B	C	D
70	A	B	C	D
71	A	B	C	D
72	A	B	C	D
73	A	B	C	D
74	A	B	C	D
75	A	B	C	D

76	A	B	C	D
77	A	B	C	D
78	A	B	C	D
79	A	B	C	D
80	A	B	C	D
81	A	B	C	D
82	A	B	C	D
83	A	B	C	D
84	A	B	C	D
85	A	B	C	D
86	A	B	C	D
87	A	B	C	D
88	A	B	C	D
89	A	B	C	D
90	A	B	C	D

EMPTY ANSWER SHEET 1

91	A	B	C	D
92	A	B	C	D
93	A	B	C	D
94	A	B	C	D
95	A	B	C	D
96	A	B	C	D
97	A	B	C	D
98	A	B	C	D
99	A	B	C	D
100	A	B	C	D
101	A	B	C	D
102	A	B	C	D
103	A	B	C	D
104	A	B	C	D
105	A	B	C	D

106	A	B	C	D
107	A	B	C	D
108	A	B	C	D
109	A	B	C	D
110	A	B	C	D
111	A	B	C	D
112	A	B	C	D
113	A	B	C	D
114	A	B	C	D
115	A	B	C	D
116	A	B	C	D
117	A	B	C	D
118	A	B	C	D
119	A	B	C	D
120	A	B	C	D

EMPTY ANSWER SHEET 1

121	A	B	C	D
122	A	B	C	D
123	A	B	C	D
124	A	B	C	D

Notes

EMPTY ANSWER SHEET 2

1	A	B	C	D
2	A	B	C	D
3	A	B	C	D
4	A	B	C	D
5	A	B	C	D
6	A	B	C	D
7	A	B	C	D
8	A	B	C	D
9	A	B	C	D
10	A	B	C	D
11	A	B	C	D
12	A	B	C	D
13	A	B	C	D
14	A	B	C	D
15	A	B	C	D

16	A	B	C	D
17	A	B	C	D
18	A	B	C	D
19	A	B	C	D
20	A	B	C	D
21	A	B	C	D
22	A	B	C	D
23	A	B	C	D
24	A	B	C	D
25	A	B	C	D
26	A	B	C	D
27	A	B	C	D
28	A	B	C	D
29	A	B	C	D
30	A	B	C	D

EMPTY ANSWER SHEET 2

31	A	B	C	D
32	A	B	C	D
33	A	B	C	D
34	A	B	C	D
35	A	B	C	D
36	A	B	C	D
37	A	B	C	D
38	A	B	C	D
39	A	B	C	D
40	A	B	C	D
41	A	B	C	D
42	A	B	C	D
43	A	B	C	D
44	A	B	C	D
45	A	B	C	D

46	A	B	C	D
47	A	B	C	D
48	A	B	C	D
49	A	B	C	D
50	A	B	C	D
51	A	B	C	D
52	A	B	C	D
53	A	B	C	D
54	A	B	C	D
55	A	B	C	D
56	A	B	C	D
57	A	B	C	D
58	A	B	C	D
59	A	B	C	D
60	A	B	C	D

EMPTY ANSWER SHEET 2

61	A	B	C	D
62	A	B	C	D
63	A	B	C	D
64	A	B	C	D
65	A	B	C	D
66	A	B	C	D
67	A	B	C	D
68	A	B	C	D
69	A	B	C	D
70	A	B	C	D
71	A	B	C	D
72	A	B	C	D
73	A	B	C	D
74	A	B	C	D
75	A	B	C	D

76	A	B	C	D
77	A	B	C	D
78	A	B	C	D
79	A	B	C	D
80	A	B	C	D
81	A	B	C	D
82	A	B	C	D
83	A	B	C	D
84	A	B	C	D
85	A	B	C	D
86	A	B	C	D
87	A	B	C	D
88	A	B	C	D
89	A	B	C	D
90	A	B	C	D

EMPTY ANSWER SHEET 2

91	A	B	C	D
92	A	B	C	D
93	A	B	C	D
94	A	B	C	D
95	A	B	C	D
96	A	B	C	D
97	A	B	C	D
98	A	B	C	D
99	A	B	C	D
100	A	B	C	D
101	A	B	C	D
102	A	B	C	D
103	A	B	C	D
104	A	B	C	D
105	A	B	C	D

106	A	B	C	D
107	A	B	C	D
108	A	B	C	D
109	A	B	C	D
110	A	B	C	D
111	A	B	C	D
112	A	B	C	D
113	A	B	C	D
114	A	B	C	D
115	A	B	C	D
116	A	B	C	D
117	A	B	C	D
118	A	B	C	D
119	A	B	C	D
120	A	B	C	D

EMPTY ANSWER SHEET 2

121	A	B	C	D
122	A	B	C	D
123	A	B	C	D
124	A	B	C	D

Notes

Notes

ANSWER KEY

Q. #	Answer		Q. #	Answer		Q. #	Answer		Q. #	Answer
1	A		16	D		31	B		46	D
2	D		17	C		32	A		47	B
3	C		18	A		33	B		48	B
4	C		19	A		34	B		49	B
5	C		20	B		35	B		50	A
6	D		21	B		36	C		51	C
7	D		22	C		37	A		52	D
8	C		23	B		38	B		53	C
9	C		24	C		39	D		54	B
10	B		25	D		40	C		55	A
11	C		26	C		41	C		56	D
12	D		27	B		42	B		57	A
13	B		28	A		43	D		58	C
14	C		29	D		44	B		59	A
15	B		30	C		45	D		60	D

ANSWER KEY

Q. #	Answer
61	A
62	B
63	A
64	C
65	C
66	B
67	A
68	D
69	A
70	A
71	D
72	C
73	B
74	C
75	C

Q. #	Answer
76	C
77	B
78	D
79	A
80	B
81	B
82	D
83	B
84	B
85	C
86	A
87	D
88	D
89	B
90	B

Q. #	Answer
91	B
92	B
93	A
94	C
95	C
96	D
97	D
98	D
99	A
100	A
101	A
102	A
103	C
104	C
105	B

Q. #	Answer
106	B
107	A
108	A
109	B
110	B
111	A
112	D
113	C
114	C
115	A
116	C
117	B
118	B
119	A
120	B

ANSWER KEY

Q. #	Answer
121	C
122	B
123	A
124	B

Notes

ORDER OTHER PARTS OF CAT I PREP I PACKAGE

Don't guess where your skill stands; certify it. PrepCertify believes that the best preparation for professional certifications is obtained through practicing well-designed real world problems.

Learn what really matters in real world industry while mastering the Body of Knowledge in the certification standards. Your Cat I Prep I series does that for you. Through PrepCertify, you will achieve your certification in a much shorter time and with a greater value of your time and effort.

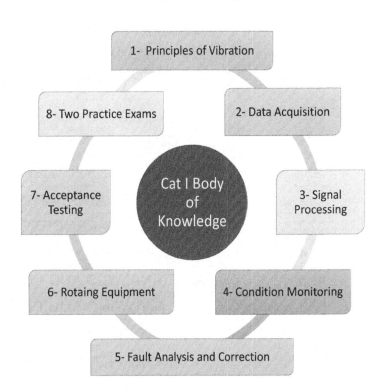

Vibration Analysis Certification Exam Preparation Package
Certified Vibration Analyst Category I
ISO 18436-2 CVA Level 1
CAT I PREP I SERIES PRACTICE TESTS

Part	Covered Body of Knowledge	ISBN-13
1	PRINCIPLES OF VIBRATION	978-1-64415-006-1
2	DATA ACQUISITION	978-1-64415-009-2
3	SIGNAL PROCESSING	978-1-64415-002-3
4	CONDITION MONITORING	978-1-64415-005-4
5	FAULT ANALYSIS AND CORRECTION	978-1-64415-008-5
6	ROTATING EQUIPMENT	978-1-64415-001-6
7	ACCEPTANCE TESTING	978-1-64415-004-7
8	TWO PRACTICE TESTS	978-1-64415-007-8

Notes

Notes

Made in the USA
Coppell, TX
12 January 2024

27630903R00096